I Love Rocks

Molly Bridger

Illustrated by Michael Chesworth

I love collecting rocks.

I like to keep them in a box.

I look high, I look low.

I find rocks wherever I go.

I love big rocks.
I love little rocks.
I love hard rocks.
I love brittle rocks.

I can't carry all my rocks.
So I put some in my socks.

Below the ground, the rocks are big.
So I have to dig and dig.

8

In caves, the rocks are long and wet.
This one is too big to get.

I find some rocks by the sea.
That is where I found these three.

I like to show rocks to my class.
This one is flat and looks like glass.

This one is white and has a ring.

This one writes on anything.

This one's beautiful – black and gold!

This one just feels nice to hold.

Now I have so many rocks,
I will need a bigger box!